Dear **Mum**

from you to me®

JOURNALS®
of a LIFETIME
made with love *from you to me*

JournalsOfALifetime.com

Dear Mum

from you to me®

This book is for your Mother's unique and amazing story.

It is for her to capture some of her life's key memories, experiences and feelings.

Ask her to complete it carefully and, if she wants to, add some photographs or images to personalise it more.

When it is finished and returned to you, this will be a record of her story . . . a story that you will treasure forever.

Dear

Here is a gift from me to you . . . for you to give to me.

When we are children we are always asking questons . . . well now I have some more for you.

Please could you answer them in the way that only you know how and then give the book back to me.

There might be a couple of questions that you prefer not to answer, so don't worry, just answer the others as well as you can . . . I won't mind.

People say that we all have at least one book in us, and this will be one of yours.

The story of you and me that I will treasure forever.

Thank you,

with love

Tell me about the time and place you were born . . .

What are your **earliest** memories?

Tell me about your **Mum** and **Dad** . . .

What do you think your parents thought of you as a child?

What **interesting** information do you know about other people in our family?

Please detail what you know of our family tree . . .

Here's some space for you to add more about our family that will interest generations to come . . .

What do you remember about the place/s you lived when you were a child?

What were your favourite childhood toys or games?

Tell me about your **best friend/s** as a young child . . .

What do you remember about your holidays as a child?

What sort of pets did you have when you were young and what were their names?

What were you best at when you were at school?

What did you want to do when you grew up?

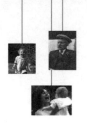

Who was your **best friend** as a teenager . . . and why?

What were your favourite hobbies when you were young?

Did you have an idol when you were young?
Tell me who and why . . .

What was the first piece of music you bought?

What piece/s of music would you **choose** in your own favourite 'top 10' from when you were young?

Describe some of the favourite outfits you wore as a young woman . . .

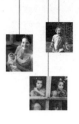

What age were you when you started work?
Tell me about the jobs you have had . . .

How did you **meet** my *Father*?

What would you do for a **night-out** when you were **dating**?

Tell me about a **special** piece of **music** that you and Dad had 'just for you' ...

Describe the occasion when you first met my Dad's parents . . .

How long had you **known** my Father when
you decided to have children?

How did you **feel** when you found out you were **pregnant** with me?

What did you think when you first saw me after I was born?

What were my **statistics** when I was born . . .
time of birth, weight, height etc?

What did I look like when I was born?
If you have a photo, could you stick it here please . . .

What was the first thing my Father said to you after I was born?

What was my **nickname** before I was born or when I was young?

Before I was born, what other names had you thought of calling me?
thought of calling me?

What was the first word or words you remember me saying?

Describe some of the favourite memories you have of me when I was a child . . .

What was I like when I was a child?

What **attributes** did I have as a child that I still have now?

What were you most **proud** of about me when I was at school?

Describe what you **like** about me . . .

Is there anything you would like to change about me?

What are the **happiest** or greatest *memories*
of your life?

What are a few of your favourite things?

Describe your memory of some major world events that have happened in your lifetime . . .

Describe the greatest change that you have seen in your lifetime so far . . .

Describe something you still want to **achieve** in your life . . .

Tell me about the **dreams** you have for your life . . .

If you were an **animal** . . . what **type** of animal would you be, and why?

If you won the Lottery . . . what would you do with the money?

What have you **found** most **difficult** in your life?

What is your **biggest regret** in your life?

Can you do anything about it now?

With hindsight what would you do differently?

Tell me something you think I won't know about you . . .

How do you like to be thought of by others?

Is there anything you would like to say sorry for?

What piece of **advice** would you like to **offer** me?

And now your chance to write anything else you want to say to me . . .

These extra pages are for us to write any
questions, memories or answers that
may not have been covered elsewhere in the book . . .

And finally for the record . . .

what is your full name ?

what is your maiden name ?

what is your date of birth ?

what colour are your eyes ?

how tall are you ?

what blood group are you ?

what was the date when you completed this story for me ?

And a few words to thank you for completing this Journal of a Lifetime ...

Dear Mum

from you to me®

First published in the UK by *from you to me*, August 2007. This edition October 2017.

Copyright, *from you to me* limited 2007
The Old Brewery, Newtown, Bradford on Avon, BA15 1NF
www.JournalsOfALifetime.com
E-mail: hello@fromyoutome.com

ISBN 978-1-907048-00-5

Cover design by so design consultants, Wick, Bristol, UK   www.so-design.co.uk
Printed and bound by Liberduplex.

This paper is manufactured from material sourced from forests certified according to strict environmental, social and economical standards.

If you think other questions should be included in future editions, please let us know. And please share some of the interesting answers you receive with us at the from you to me website to let other people read about these fascinating insights . . .

MIX
Paper from
responsible sources
FSC® C109440